Ready to Learn
BEGINNING MATH

by Imogene Forte

Incentive Publications, Inc.
Nashville, Tennessee

Illustrated by Gayle Harvey
Cover by Geoffrey Brittingham
Edited by Charlotte Bosarge

ISBN 0-86530-594-3

PRINTED IN THE UNITED STATES OF AMERICA
www.incentivepublications.com

Table of Contents

To Parents and Teachers

Why You Need This Book

- The Ready to Learn books capitalize on the vitally important "teachable" years from 4 to 6.

- Basic skills and concepts are introduced to help pave the way to increased self-confidence and reinforced lifelong learning success.

What Children Will Learn From This Book

- Children will learn the following basic math skills and concepts which are so important to early learning success:

    o *Recognizing Numerals*

    o *Writing Numerals*

    o *Counting Numerals*

    o *Counting by Sets*

    o *Matching Sets*

    o *Matching Numerals and Sets*

    o *Using Size Words*

    o *Discriminating Between **Large** and **Small***

    o *Discriminating Between **Long** and **Short***

    o *Discriminating Between **Long**, **Longer**, and **Longest***

    o *Discriminating Between **Big** and **Little***

How to Get the Most From This Book

- Read and interpret the directions for the child.

- Keep the atmosphere light and relaxed.

- Allow the child to work at his or her own pace, free from pressure to perform.

- Praise the child's efforts!

Skills Checklist

Beginning
Math

Meet Monty Monkey

Meet Monty Monkey.

He is learning to read numerals from **1** to **10**.

Can you help?

Color the numerals red and say their names.

Recognizing Numerals 1 to 10

*Ready To Learn Series — **Beginning Math***
Copyright ©2003 by Incentive Publications, Inc., Nashville, TN.

Mindy Monkey

Monty Monkey's friend Mindy Monkey is learning to read the number words **one** to **ten**.
Can you help?

Color the number words blue and say their names.

1

How many monkeys are in this picture?

Color the monkeys brown.

Practice writing the numeral **1**:

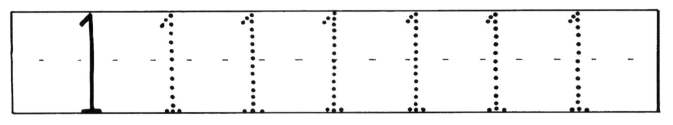

Recognizing and Writing
*the **Numeral 1***

*Ready To Learn Series — **Beginning Math***
Copyright ©2003 by Incentive Publications, Inc., Nashville, TN.

One

Monty has
one banana.

Color the
banana yellow.

Practice writing the word **one**:

one one one

2

Monty's friend Merry has come to play.

How many monkeys will play?

Practice writing the numeral **2**:

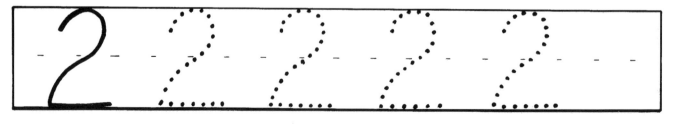

Two

Monty and Merry love to play ball.
How many balls do they have?

Color one ball blue.
Color one ball green.

Practice writing the word **two**:

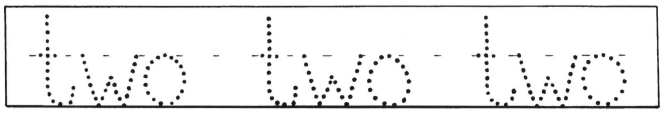

3

Max Monkey wants to play ball too.

How many monkeys are playing the game?

Practice writing the numeral **3**:

 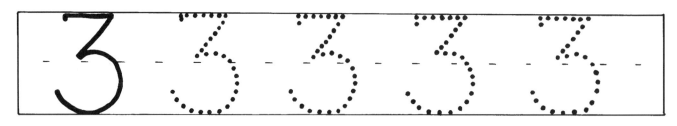

Three

Max brought his own ball.

How many balls do Monty, Merry, and Max have?

Color one ball blue, one ball green, and one ball red.

Practice writing the word **three**:

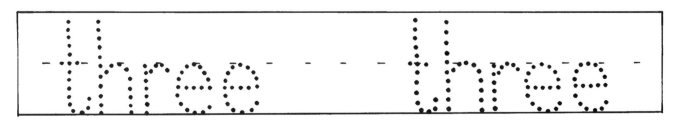

4

Merry's cousin Mel Monkey came by for a visit.

How many monkeys are playing now?

Practice writing the numeral 4:

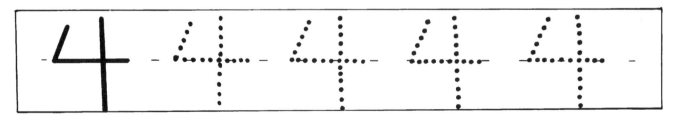

Four

Mel brought his own ball.
How many balls do the monkeys have now?
Color one ball blue, one ball green, one ball red,
and one ball yellow.

Practice writing the word **four**:

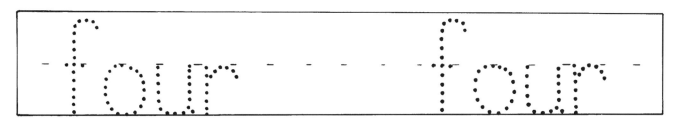

5

Mamie Monkey brought a bigger ball.

How many monkeys are there now?

Practice writing the numeral **5**:

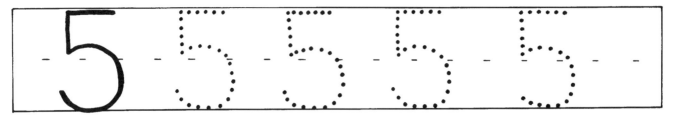

Recognizing and Writing
the Numeral 5

Ready To Learn Series — Beginning Math

Five

How many balls are in the game now?

Draw **five** dots on the biggest ball.

Practice writing the word **five**:

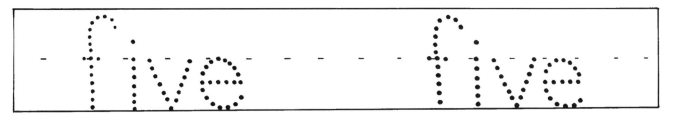

6

Minnie Monkey came for lunch.

How many monkeys are there now?

Practice writing the numeral **6**:

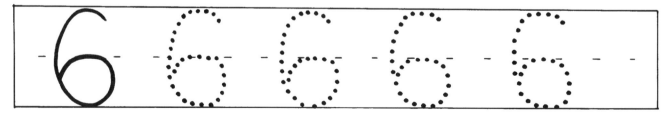

Six

Minnie brought the food.

How many lunches did Minnie bring?

Practice writing the word **six**:

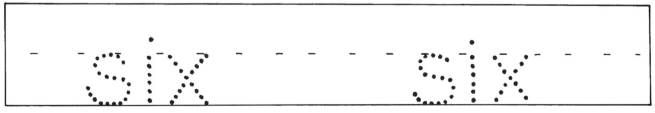

7

Moses Monkey brought lemonade.
How many monkeys are there now?
Color 4 monkeys black.
Color 3 monkeys brown.

Practice writing the numeral **7**:

Recognizing and Writing
the **Numeral 7**

*Ready To Learn Series — **Beginning Math***
Copyright ©2003 by Incentive Publications, Inc., Nashville, TN.

Seven

All the monkeys are thirsty.

How many glasses of lemonade did Moses bring?

Practice writing the word **seven**:

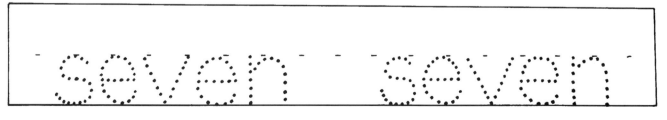

8

Manny Monkey brought bananas.
How many monkeys are there now?

Color the bananas yellow.

Practice writing the numeral **8**:

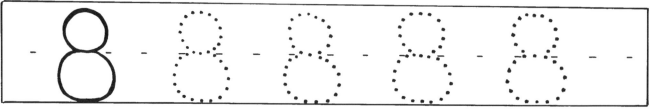

Eight

All the monkeys love bananas.

How many monkeys are eating bananas?

Practice writing the word **eight**:

9

Megan Monkey came late.

How many monkeys are there now?

Practice writing the numeral **9**:

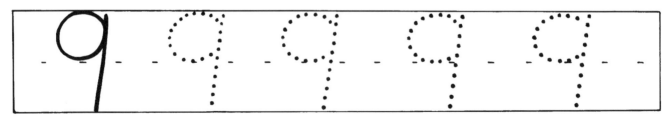

*Recognizing and Writing
the* **Numeral 9**

Ready To Learn Series — **Beginning Math**
Copyright ©2003 by Incentive Publications, Inc., Nashville, TN.

Nine

Megan came just in time to help clean up.

How many monkeys are working?

Draw a trash can under the tree to help the monkeys clean up.

Practice writing the word **nine**:

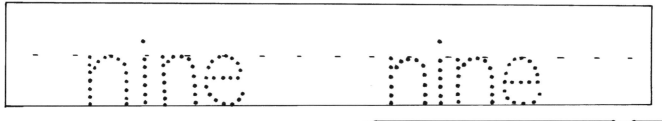

10

Madeline Monkey came last.

How many monkeys are there now?

Practice writing the numeral **10**:

10 -10 -10 -10

Recognizing and Writing the Numeral 10

Ready To Learn Series — Beginning Math
Copyright ©2003 by Incentive Publications, Inc., Nashville, TN.

Ten

Now there are **ten** monkeys.

It's time for the game to begin.
Which team do you think will win?

Practice writing the word **ten**:

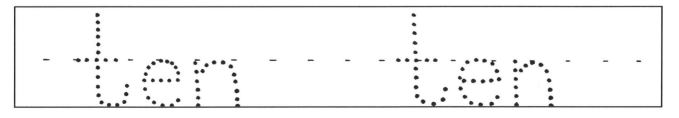

0

0 means **having none**.

Monty Monkey had three bananas.

He gave one to Merry Monkey.

Megan Monkey also got one banana.

He gave the third banana to Madeline Monkey.

Now Monty Monkey has no bananas.

Monty has **none** at all.

Practice writing the numeral **0**:

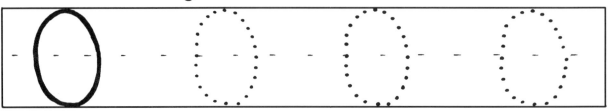

Ready To Learn Series — Beginning Math
Copyright ©2003 by Incentive Publications, Inc., Nashville, TN.

1, 2, 3, 4, 5

Color the numeral **1** blue.

Color the numeral **2** orange.

Color the numeral **3** green.

Color the numeral **4** yellow.

Color the numeral **5** red.

6, 7, 8, 9, 10

Color the numeral **6** green.

Color the numeral **7** blue.

Color the numeral **8** red.

Color the numeral **9** orange.

Color the numeral **10** yellow.

*Ready To Learn Series — **Beginning Math***
Copyright ©2003 by Incentive Publications, Inc., Nashville, TN.

Monkeys with Spots

Read the numeral under each monkey.

Draw that many spots on that monkey.

1

2

3

4

5

Find 1, 2, 3, 4, 5

Find the numerals **1, 2, 3, 4,** and **5** in the puzzle.

Color the numerals red.

Find 6, 7, 8, 9, and 10

Find the numerals **6, 7, 8, 9,** and **10** in the puzzle.

Color the numerals blue.

Find and Color the Numerals

From 1 to 10, all the numerals are hiding from you.

Find and color all 10 numerals blue.

Ready To Learn Series — **Beginning Math**
Copyright ©2003 by Incentive Publications, Inc., Nashville, TN.

1, 2, 3

How many?
Count the monkeys in each set.

Trace the numerals.

 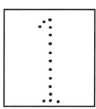

 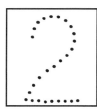

 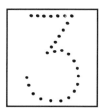

4, 5, 6

How many?
Count the monkeys in each set.

Trace the numerals.

 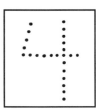

 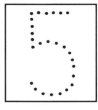

 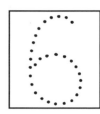

7 and 8

How many?
Count the monkeys in each set.

Trace the numerals.

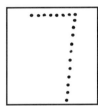

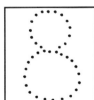

9 and 10

How many?
Count the monkeys in each set.

Trace the numerals.

 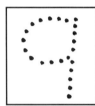

 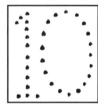

Ready To Learn Series — **Beginning Math**
Copyright ©2003 by Incentive Publications, Inc., Nashville, TN.

Monkeys in the Trees

Monty Monkey and his friends love to play hide and seek.

Read the numeral on each tree trunk.
Find and circle that many monkeys hiding in the tree.

Draw a line to the matching number word.

Two   One   Four   Three

Fun in the Sun

Count to find out how many of each kind of animal is having fun in the sun.

Write the correct numeral in each box.

Frogs

Snakes

Turtles

How many monkeys are under the tree?

Count the Treats

Draw a line from each box to the numeral that tells how many treats are in the box.

7   5   4   3

Follow the Dots

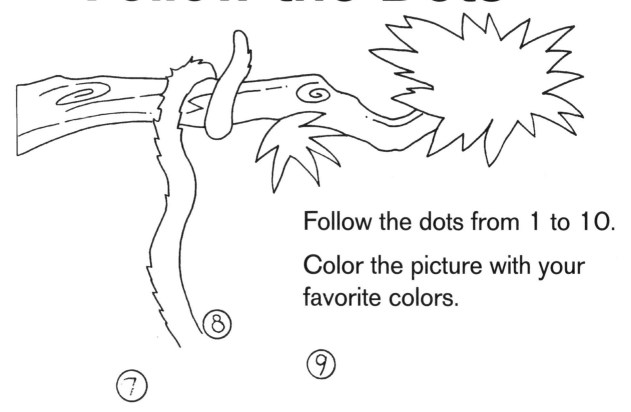

Follow the dots from 1 to 10.

Color the picture with your favorite colors.

*Ready To Learn Series — **Beginning Math***
Copyright ©2003 by Incentive Publications, Inc., Nashville, TN.

Monkey Sets

A **set** is a group of things that are alike and together.

This is a set of
two monkeys.

Two monkeys are in the set.

Write the numeral. _____

This is a set of
three monkeys.

Three monkeys are in the set.

Write the numeral. _____

This is a set of
four monkeys.

Four monkeys are in the set.

Write the numeral. _____

This is a set of
five monkeys.

Five monkeys are in the set.

Write the numeral. _____

More Monkey Sets

A **set** is a group of things that are alike and together.

This is a set of **six** monkeys.

Six monkeys are in the set.

Write the numeral. _____

This is a set of **seven** monkeys.

Seven monkeys are in the set.

Write the numeral. _____

This is a set of
eight monkeys.

Eight monkeys
are in the set.

Write the numeral. _____

This is a set of
nine monkeys.

Nine monkeys
are in the set.

Write the numeral. _____

*Ready To Learn Series — **Beginning Math***
Copyright ©2003 by Incentive Publications, Inc., Nashville, TN.

How Many Monkeys?

How many are in each set?

Write the numeral. _____

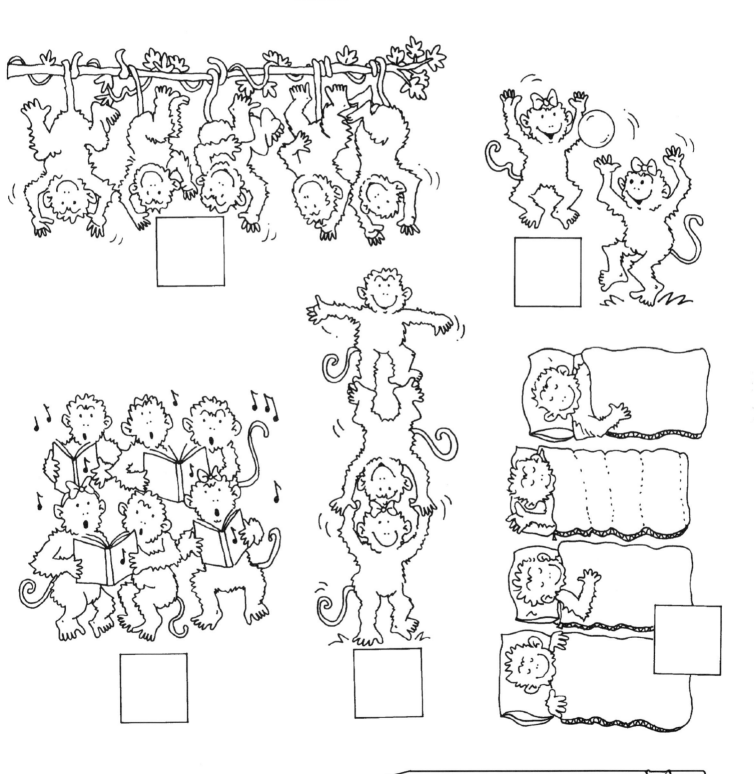

*Ready To Learn Series — **Beginning Math***
Copyright ©2003 by Incentive Publications, Inc., Nashville, TN.

Pairs

A **pair** is a set of two things that go together.

This is one foot.   This is one pair of feet.

Match each numeral with a set of pairs.

one pair   two pairs   three pairs

*Ready To Learn Series — **Beginning Math***
Copyright ©2003 by Incentive Publications, Inc., Nashville, TN.

Matching Sets of Spots

Draw lines to connect three pairs of monkeys who have matching **sets** of spots.

Color the other monkeys.

Counting by Sets

How many are in each **set**?

Write the numeral in the box.

Ready To Learn Series — *Beginning Math*
Copyright ©2003 by Incentive Publications, Inc., Nashville, TN.

Monty's Sets

Complete the picture of Monty Monkey by drawing these **sets** on his body:

- A set of three spots
- A pair of eyes
- A set of two feet
- A pair of hands
- A pair of ears

Size Words

An elephant is **large**.
A mouse is **small**.

Make an X on the picture of the largest monkey.

Draw a circle around the smallest monkey.

Color the smallest butterfly.

 Recognizing and Using Size Words:
Large and *Small*

*Ready To Learn Series — **Beginning Math***
Copyright ©2003 by Incentive Publications, Inc., Nashville, TN.

Large

This picture shows three **large** things.
Another word for **large** is **big**.

– Color the large elephant green.

– Color the large tree brown.

– Color the large rock black.

– Draw one more large thing in the picture.

Big

Marty Monkey is a very big Monkey.
Write the word **big**.

big

Draw and color 3 big things.

| Recognizing and Writing the Word **Big**

Ready To Learn Series — **Beginning Math**
Copyright ©2003 by Incentive Publications, Inc., Nashville, TN.

Small Things

This picture shows things that are **small**.

Another word for **small** is **little**.

Draw a circle around the **little** monkey.

Color five other **little** things.

Ben Little

Ben Little is a little baby bunny.
Trace and write the word **little**.

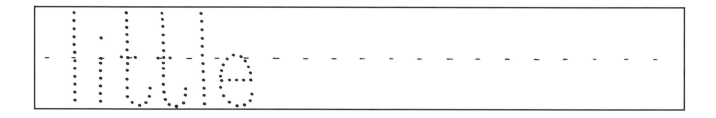

Draw and color 5 little things.

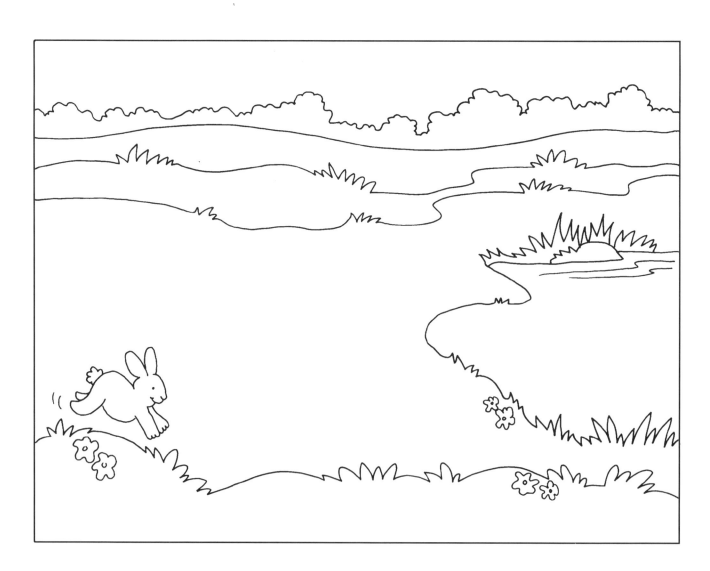

*Ready To Learn Series — **Beginning Math***
Copyright ©2003 by Incentive Publications, Inc., Nashville, TN.

Big and Little

Find a **little** nest for the **little** bird.
Color the **little** nest brown.

Find a **big** nest for a **big** bird.
Color the **big** nest orange.

Draw lines to match each bird with the correct nest.

More Size Words

A man's shoe is **long**.
A baby's shoe is **short**.
Color the picture of the girl with the **longest** hair.
Draw a circle around the picture of the girl
with the **shortest** hair.

 Recognizing and Using Size Words

Ready To Learn Series — Beginning Math
Copyright ©2003 by Incentive Publications, Inc., Nashville, TN.

Long and Short

A snake is **long**.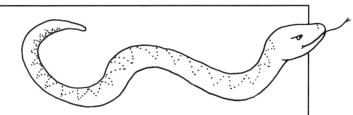

A tadpole is **short**.

A dragon's foot is **long**.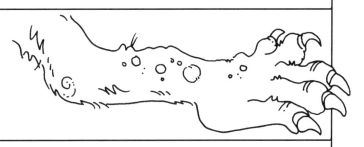

A frog's foot is **short**.

Place your foot beside a grownup's foot.
Which is shorter?

Color the **long** things green.

Color the **short** things yellow.

Monty Monkey's Party

It is Monty Monkey's Birthday.

Count the candles on the cake to see how old he is.

Make an X on the **shortest** banana.

Color the **largest** cup cake red.

Color a **set** of 3 balloons blue.

Draw a picture to fit in the box of something Monty would like for a birthday present.

*Ready To Learn Series — **Beginning Math***
Copyright ©2003 by Incentive Publications, Inc., Nashville, TN.

More Things to Do

Activities and Projects to Help Young Children Learn about Beginning Math

- Look around for objects to count. Try using fun things like raisins, cereal, apples, or oranges. Use your imagination to make up counting games that are fun but also educational.
  For example:

  √ Ask the child to group the objects by size, shape or color. Then count the objects in each group as well as the number of groups.

  √ Make up stories about the objects and play simple addition and subtraction games.
  For example: The baby bear ate two apples, the papa bear ate three apples. How many apples in all were eaten?

- Play measuring games. Give the child a big bowl, measuring cups and spoons and plenty of space. Teach the children to measure, pour, add to or take away. Then help the child to make muffins or cookies if possible.

- Pick a number to be the theme for the day. Help the child make a number book out of buttons and construction paper. Paste the correct number of buttons beside each numeral.

- Make number word flash cards from tag board or index cards. Cut out corresponding cards with groups of objects drawn on them. Help the child use the cards to:
  - Identify sets
  - Identify number words
  - Count by sets
  - Match numbers with groups of objects

- Direct the child to identify objects around the room as large, small, big, little, short, or long. Help the child use a ruler to "measure" the differences in size by putting a little mark on the yardstick for each object.